DISNEY · PIXAR

BRAVE

enix international publications, inc

Merida is fed up with all her lessons! She leaves the castle behind and finds freedom in the forest with her horse, Angus. Search for these falcons, whose mothers never tell them what to do!

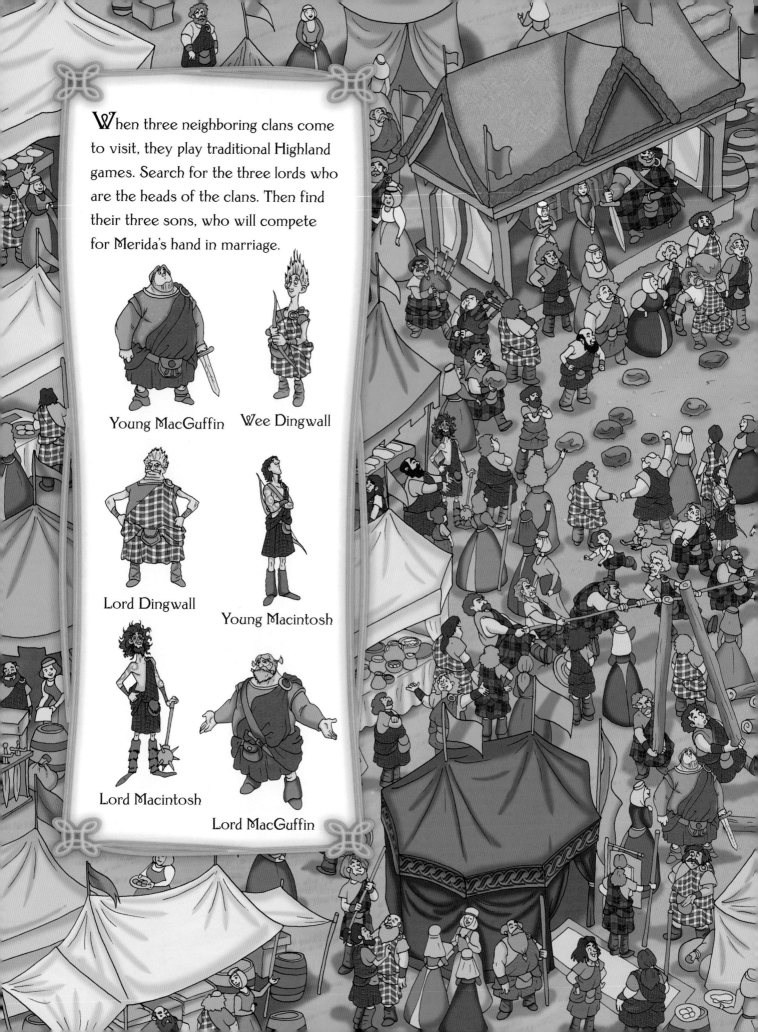

When three neighboring clans come to visit, they play traditional Highland games. Search for the three lords who are the heads of the clans. Then find their three sons, who will compete for Merida's hand in marriage.

Young MacGuffin

Wee Dingwall

Lord Dingwall

Young Macintosh

Lord Macintosh

Lord MacGuffin

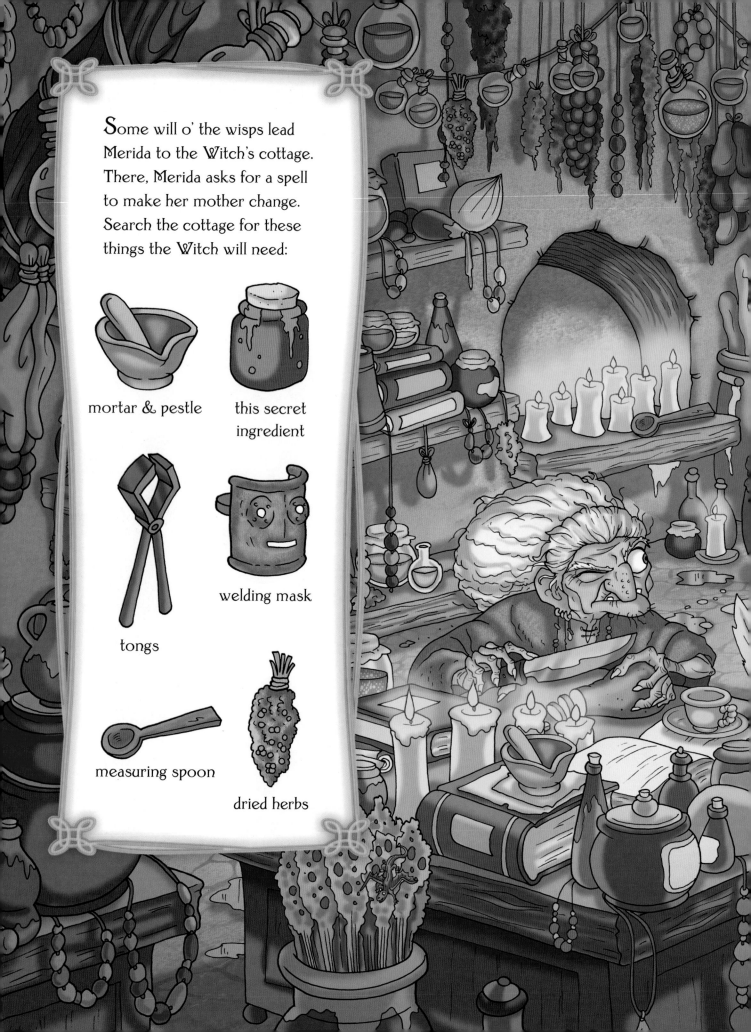

Some will o' the wisps lead Merida to the Witch's cottage. There, Merida asks for a spell to make her mother change. Search the cottage for these things the Witch will need:

mortar & pestle

this secret ingredient

tongs

welding mask

measuring spoon

dried herbs

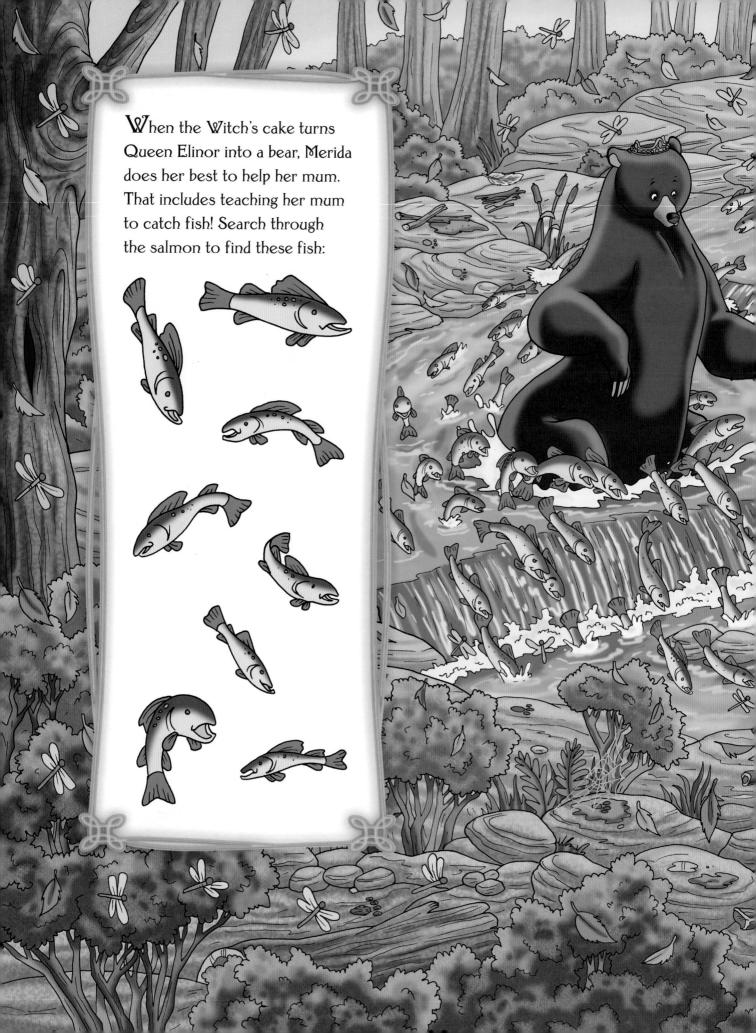

When the Witch's cake turns Queen Elinor into a bear, Merida does her best to help her mum. That includes teaching her mum to catch fish! Search through the salmon to find these fish:

Inside Mor'du's lair, Merida realizes that the bear was once a rebellious prince who asked the Witch for the strength of ten men. Search the castle ruins for these ancient carvings:

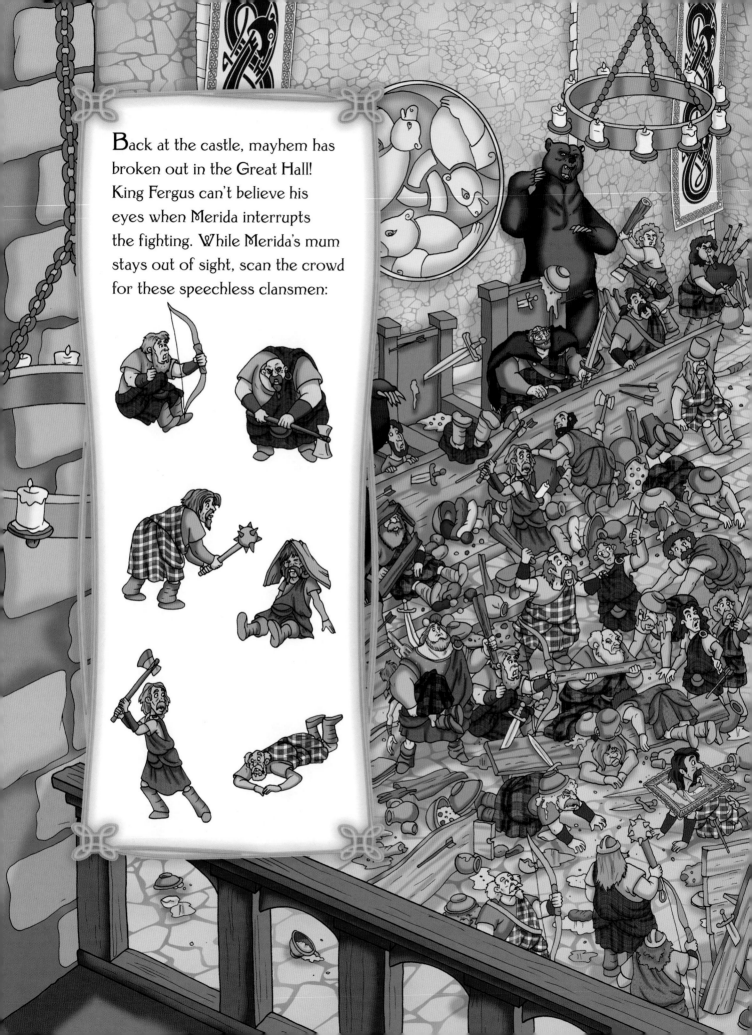

Back at the castle, mayhem has broken out in the Great Hall! King Fergus can't believe his eyes when Merida interrupts the fighting. While Merida's mum stays out of sight, scan the crowd for these speechless clansmen:

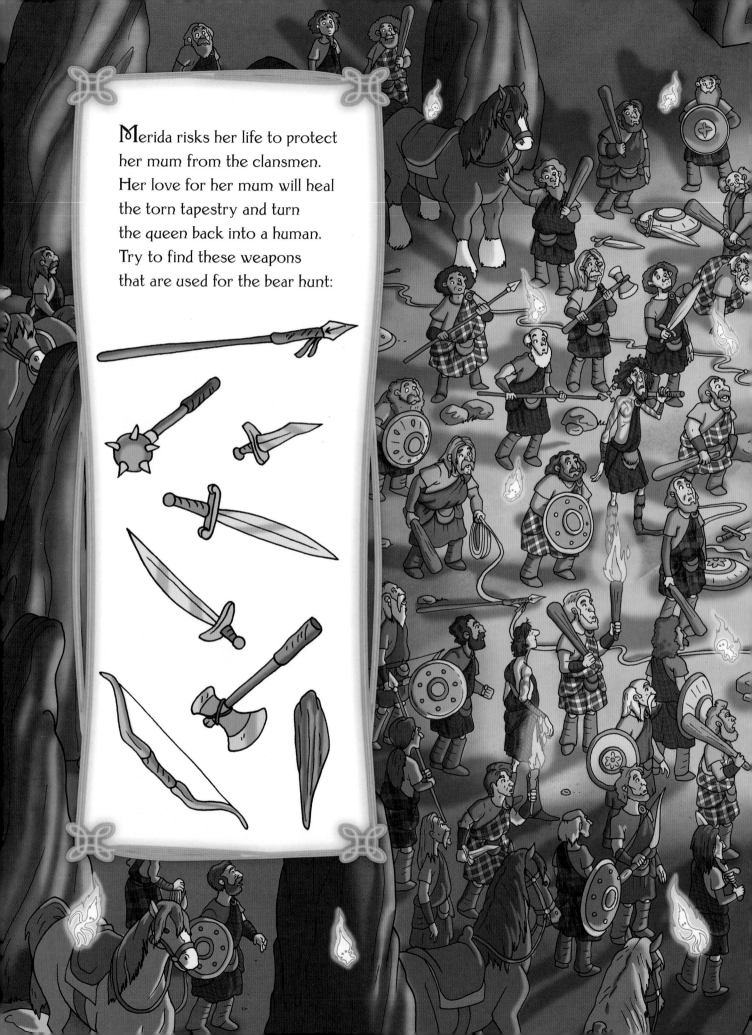

Merida risks her life to protect her mum from the clansmen. Her love for her mum will heal the torn tapestry and turn the queen back into a human. Try to find these weapons that are used for the bear hunt:

Merida and her mum will work together to create a new tapestry. And now Merida will have the chance to create her own future. Look around the Tapestry Room to find these figures from the past:

maiden

deerhound

falcon

this horse

this horse

deer

knight

Return to Merida's archery
practice to find these targets
that she has made for herself:

Run back to the Highland
Games to find these
athletes and performers:

Fly back to the Witch's cottage
to track down these things:

Return to the river to find
these signs of wildlife:

Sneak back to Mor'du's lair to find these things from long ago, when Mor'du was still a prince:

Go back to the Great Hall to find these things that have been turned into weapons:

Float back to the bear hunt and count all the will o' the wisps like these you can find:

Return to the Tapestry Room to find these sewing supplies: